ITHORIAN
INVASION

STAR WARS®
MISSIONS

#7
ITHORIAN INVASION

DAVE WOLVERTON

SCHOLASTIC INC.
New York   Toronto   London   Auckland   Sydney

ISBN 0-590-12047-6

12 11 10 9 8 7 6 5 4 3 2 1   8 9/9 0 1 2 3/0

Printed in the U.S.A.

First Scholastic printing, March 1998

ITHORIAN INVASION

PRELIMINARY MISSION

CHAPTER ONE

There were times when Han Solo wished that the *Millennium Falcon* was big enough to have a cloaking device. Right now was definitely one of those times.

The *Falcon* was coming up on the planet Ithor, a lush jungle world. It was the home of the peaceful Ithorians, or Hammerheads, as they were sometimes called. The only problem was that the "peaceful" planet was home to two Imperial Star Destroyers. Even one of the enormous ships would have been too many. Two were almost enough to quell a major uprising — almost enough to launch an invasion.

And if *that* wasn't enough, Solo could see a couple hundred TIE fighters buzzing between the Star Destroyers, part of the Empire's complex training maneuvers.

"If these Imperials spot us, we're dead," Princess Leia warned. She stood in the cockpit, behind Solo and his co-pilot Chewbacca, beside the Ithorian Momaw Nadon. Luke was in the gun bay, in case some TIE fighters got too close. The droids See-Threepio and Artoo-Detoo were at a repair station, testing circuitry.

"Believe me," Solo said. "If they spot us, I'm getting out of here."

"I beg you," Momaw Nadon pleaded, "do not leave my world too quickly. We are in dire need of your assistance. Your Rebel cohorts have promised to clear these ships away by noon tomorrow." The Ithorian had two mouths — one on each side of his long curved neck. He spoke with both mouths at once, so that his words came out in stereo. It made a distinctly odd sound.

"Don't worry," Leia said, "the Rebel Alliance won't desert you in your hour of need." Then she added harshly, "Will they, Solo?"

Solo licked his lips. The *Falcon* was fitted with an Imperial transponder, a device that identified Solo's ship as an Imperial diplomatic shuttle, carrying a minor official down to the planet. So far, everything was going great . . .

. . . But if any of the TIE fighters got close enough to the *Falcon*, they would know by the shape of the ship that it wasn't a diplomatic shuttle.

Solo released a ragged breath. "I don't think we can make it down there. I don't care what Admiral Ackbar says — this isn't going to work."

"It *must* work," Momaw Nadon said. Solo glanced up at the Ithorian. He was dressed in a simple clerical robe. He didn't *look* like a grand revolutionary leader. Yet the Rebel Alliance thought it imperative to deliver him to his home planet. The peaceful Ithorians were on the verge of revolt against the Empire, but they needed someone to lead them in their fight. Momaw Nadon was the Ithorian for the job.

A message came into the *Falcon* from a Star Destroyer. "Imperial shuttle, what is your cargo and destination?"

Solo started to speak, but was interrupted as Leia clapped a hand over his mouth and whispered, "You're never any good at this. Let me do the talking."

She spoke into the microphone. "Our destination is the Ithorian herdship, the *Tafanda Bay*. Our cargo is a diplomat, Master Torturer Sir Vengnar Heiff."

For a nervous moment they waited for approval. Sir Vengnar Heiff was ruthless and efficient, the Empire's finest torturer. He was often called to extract sensitive information from Rebel leaders.

"Ah," came a tense voice over the communicator, "we have been expecting Sir Heiff. Admiral Greeb wishes to know if he would like to dine on our ship before completing his mission."

Great, Solo thought. *These folks were expecting the Torturer, and now they want to have a dinner party.*

"No," Leia said after a moment, as if she'd consulted with someone. "Sir Heiff is eager to get to work."

The voice that came over the communicator sounded relieved. "Admiral Greeb regrets that Sir Heiff is so busy, but he understands. There is much to be done on the planet. Proceed to the *Tafanda Bay*. We'll let them know that you are coming."

"Go ahead," Leia told Solo. "Go in for a landing."

Solo was having second thoughts. "Are you sure? They're expecting the Torturer down on the *Tafanda Bay*. When Sir Heiff doesn't show up in about half an hour, they'll know something is wrong. It could be a lot harder getting off this rock than getting on."

Solo imagined himself in a dogfight, trying to escape from Ithor. He'd just got the *Falcon* in top running condition. He didn't want to see his ship get all shot up.

But still — he had been told that Grubba the Hutt was on Ithor. And if Solo ever wanted to get Jabba the Hutt's bounty off his head, he'd need the younger Hutt as a bargaining chip. Even if it meant certain trouble. . . .

The Ithorian Momaw Nadon put his hand on Solo's shoulder. "Please . . . for my people."

And for Grubba. . . .

Solo dove toward the planet, muttering under his breath, "I hope we all live to regret this."

Aboard the Ithorian herdship *Tafanda Bay*, Dengar strolled with the bounty hunters Udin and Eron Stonefield through a lush ecology dome. Grubba the Hutt was safely captured. The *Tafanda Bay* was more than a ship. It was a city where hundreds of thousands of Ithorians dwelt, the largest of its kind. It was the Ithorians' greatest achievement. The Ithorians prided themselves on living harmoniously with their environment.

The dome held giant pools of water. The Ithorians had bred lilies for hundreds of generations, so that their enormous blossoms came in a rainbow of colors. Their gentle fragrance perfumed the dome.

The Imperial General Olan Dewes, a tall young man, was showing off the *Tafanda Bay*, which he had recently captured for the Empire. "This dome holds some of the more sacred of the Ithorian plants," he informed the bounty hunters. "The giant lilies are beautiful to look at, but it is the roots of the plants that intrigue the Empire. You see, the lilies anchor their roots to underwater stones using a powerful natural glue. This glue is one key to the manufacture of Ithorian leafships, the small skimmers that you may have seen outside the city. The cement is mixed with cut fibers from leaves to form a remarkably light, armored surface. We are testing it now for use on our Imperial speeders."

"Fascinating," Dengar said. As a swoop racer, he was intrigued with new ways to armor fast vehicles.

An aide stepped up to Dewes. "General, we have a problem. The Torturer is here."

"Here? Now?" the general asked in dismay, paling at the news. In all the Empire, few men had as nasty a reputation as Heiff's.

Dengar had worked with Heiff before, and was not impressed. The man was a butcher. It only showed how little the Empire valued the peaceful Ithorians, if they sent Heiff to do their dirty work.

"His shuttle just cleared security," the aide replied.

"Thank you," the general said. "Prepare the grand dining hall." The aide hurried off.

"Sir Heiff?" Dengar asked. "Why is he here?"

Dewes stiffened. He clearly did not want Heiff on his planet. "Some Ithorian technicians have been reluctant to reveal information. To them, the knowledge gained from the trees is not merely secret — it is sacred. Aside from a few tree-planting ceremonies, they don't set foot in the jungles of their world. They are angry that our Imperial scholars have done so. I mentioned this in my reports, and the Empire chose to send Heiff."

Dengar was not an emotional man. In fact, he no longer had certain emotions at all. No fear, no love. Yet he noted the reactions of the others. General Dewes seemed embarrassed and sickened. Eron Stonefield went white with shock. Even Udin drew back a pace in horror.

General Dewes said, "I only hope that the Ithorian prisoners divulge their information soon. As I told my superiors when they ordered him here, 'We want information — not corpses.'"

CHAPTER TWO

Luke Skywalker studied the TIE fighters' maneuvers as Han Solo dropped toward Ithor, calling out, "Mayday, Mayday! We're gonna crash!" over his communicator.

He let the ship hurtle toward the planet, pulled by gravity, as if it were spinning completely out of control. He planned to fake a crash on the planet.

As they screamed toward the ground, Solo said, "All right, now we put one little missile into the middle of those trees, and by the time the Empire discovers that there isn't a wrecked ship down there, we'll be long gone." Solo armed the missile and reached for the button to launch it.

Momaw Nadon lurched for Solo's hand, pulling it back. "No!" he shouted.

Solo looked up.

"Those trees are sacred!" the Ithorian explained.

Solo seemed to think about it a moment.

"Aaaaaaaaaagh!" he shouted over his communicator as the *Falcon* swept toward the ground. When he was close enough to the ground, he stopped shouting and turned off the communicator and the transponder at the same moment. The Empire would pinpoint the spot as the last point of contact for the crashing ship.

Solo shook his head in exasperation. "The Empire won't believe we crashed if they don't see something go boom."

"It will be all right," Luke said.

Solo pulled the *Falcon* up and let it skim the tops of the trees until he found an opening in the forest's canopy.

"Whatever you say," he replied.

The ship skimmed the surface of a wide yellow river. Atop the river was a flock of furry creatures with enormous feet and small wings. They stood on the water with wings spread and let the wind push them over the waves.

Luke had never seen a creature so naturally adapted to sailing. It was his first peek at the wonders of Ithor.

Solo flew downriver thirty miles, until he saw a peninsula reach out into the water. On top of the peninsula was a tall building of stone, a shrine with towers and a landing spot. Several Ithorians in white robes stood atop the highest tower, waving purple streamers.

"There," Momaw Nadon said. "Stop there. The landing bay is beneath the tower."

Solo slowed, banking around the tower and bringing the *Millennium Falcon* down beneath the overhang of an ancient roof. The ship was now hidden beneath a shelf of rock.

Luke and the others were soon outside, where the moist jungle air felt cool and inviting. Several Ithorians rushed into the room where the *Falcon* lay hidden. A painted tarpaulin hung above the entrance. The Ithorians pulled on some ties, causing the tarpaulin to fall and cover the opening. The ship was now in a dark room. From the outside, it would look as if this ancient shrine were solid stone. The Imperials wouldn't be able to find the *Falcon*.

Momaw Nadon stepped from the *Falcon*. One Ithorian, a woman, gave a startled cry and rushed to him. Momaw hugged her tenderly as she burst into tears.

"You're back," she said, nuzzling her eye stalk against

his. "You're home, after all these years. I waited for you, as I promised."

"I am back," Momaw Nadon soothed, "and I shall not leave you again."

Momaw Nadon looked over the woman's shoulder and saw Luke Skywalker. He squinted, an Ithorian expression of joy. "Luke Skywalker, my friend," Momaw Nadon said. "I want you to meet my wife, Fandomar."

Luke watched the tearful reunion and felt desolate. He thought of his uncle Owen and aunt Beru, the only family he had ever known. He wished that he could hold his aunt now, as Momaw Nadon held his wife.

A young Ithorian sidled up to them. He looked just like his father. Luke already knew his name: Do-Forow Nadon. "Ah, how you have grown!" Momaw Nadon rejoiced.

"Look, I'm glad you're having a happy reunion," Solo interrupted, "but we really need to get out of here. So if you would just point the way to your herdship, we'll drop you off and be on our way. There's a certain Hutt I need to find — *immediately.*"

Momaw Nadon shook his head. "We must consult the Oracle and discover how to get back. We cannot simply fly there."

"The Oracle?" Solo asked. "What is that?"

Suddenly, in the passage behind Han Solo, a tall old Ithorian appeared. His hairs had gone white, and he wore a white robe, belted with twisted vines. His eyes, too, were a pale milky color. The eyes had been burned. Luke felt an immediate jolt of recognition. Though he had never seen the Ithorian before, he had felt his kind of presence before — in Obi-Wan Kenobi. This Ithorian was powerful in the Force.

"The Oracle is not a what," the old Ithorian corrected. "It is a who."

Momaw pointed to the old man and simply said, "The Oracle."

In the failing sun, the Oracle led Luke and the others through the dense jungle. Though the old man was blind, he lifted his feet to avoid tripping on roots, and ducked for low branches more flawlessly than did those who trusted sight to navigate through the thick foliage.

Night was falling, yet Luke detected a faint blue light that suffused the woods.

"This is a sacred place," the Oracle explained. "The Bafforr trees have grown here for thousands of years. If you open your minds, you can speak to them."

"Not all people can hear them," Momaw Nadon warned. "The voices of trees can only be heard by those who have the ears to hear."

"You think not?" the Oracle said. "Surely, *all* can hear them."

"You are old," Momaw Nadon said to the Oracle. "You hear them well, and thus think that all can hear them."

"Mmmmm . . ." the old one answered. "Perhaps. . . ."

"What do the voices of the trees say?" See-Threepio piped up from the back of the line. "I myself am fluent in over six million forms of communication, but I am afraid that I have no information on how to speak with your trees."

"The trees say," Momaw Nadon answered, "that we must learn the ways of peace. They say they are in pain."

"In pain?" Leia asked. "Why?"

"This grove is very ancient, and very large," the Oracle answered. "Three days' walk from here, the Empire is rooting up trees."

"Whatever for?" See-Threepio asked. "Is the wood valuable?"

"The trees have long been our counselors," the Oracle replied. "They taught us to live in harmony with nature. The trees are wise, and the Empire hopes to learn from them."

"However," Momaw Nadon warned, "it is not as easy to learn from them as the Empire hopes. Each tree in this forest is like a single cell in your brain. The roots of the trees intertwine, connecting them, so that they form a vast intelligence. By removing a tree, the Empire severs it from its brothers. Such trees are far more alone than any human could ever be. Their pain is extreme."

"That's so cruel," Leia said. "We once had laws to protect such creatures — in the Old Republic."

"The Empire does not respect such laws," Momaw Nadon mourned. "They hope to plant the trees on foreign worlds and raise new groves from their seeds. We must stop them."

"Stop them?" the Oracle asked. "How would you do that? The Empire has heard my pleas. They will not stop."

"Of course they will not stop!" Momaw Nadon yelled. "They do not respect your wishes. They blinded you and threw you into the jungle to die."

The Oracle objected, "I am fine. The trees show me where to place my feet, where to find food."

"But the Empire would not have it that way," Momaw Nadon sighed. "You are alive in spite of their will, not because of it."

In the distance, Luke heard a flutelike noise. A piping deeper and more resonant than that made by any whistle — and its tune was far more complex. Momaw Nadon said it was the song of an arrak snake, a winged reptile that nested in the trees. Suddenly, the trees above them filled with the sound of horns, the songs of the snakes. They sang in harmony, with some snakes crying out in complex counterpoint, until it seemed that the whole sky was filled with the fascinating alien symphony. Luke was mesmerized by the sound.

"Why have you returned?" the Oracle asked Momaw Nadon softly, as if in respect for the snake's song.

"You know the answer. I have come to fight. Even the gardener must uproot weeds in his labor."

"Taking a life is not the answer," the Oracle said. "You cannot uproot the Empire. They are like the claw vine over there —" The Oracle pointed to a plant barely visible in the forest, with leaves shaped like raking claws. "You may pull it up, but its roots are far, far deeper than they seem. Pull up the plant, and the vine will simply return in greater numbers."

"I have friends in the Rebel Alliance," Momaw Nadon said. "Together, we can uproot the Empire."

The Oracle stopped and turned, looking toward Momaw Nadon in wonder. "The roots of the Empire can be found in every human heart. They are found in greed and lust and fear. How can you hope to uproot that?"

Luke thought this sounded like something Obi-Wan Kenobi would say.

Solo spoke up. "Well, I don't know if I can uproot the Empire, like you say. But with any good blaster, I can sure blow a few nuts out of its trees."

The Oracle turned sharply and pointed a warning finger at Solo. "Beware, young man. Do not judge the Empire so hastily. Not everyone who wears an Imperial uniform is wholly given to evil."

"I'll try to keep that in mind," Solo said, "next time the Imperials try to blast my head off."

The Oracle folded his arms. He looked at Solo sternly, then studied the rest of the group.

"The Bafforr have spoken. They have shown me where you can meet the *Tafanda Bay*. The ship will drop low in the hills not far from here, harvesting forrolow berries and leaves. You will be able to board the ship there. But the trees do not want a blood bath. It pains them when we do violence to one another. Not all of you can go to help smuggle Momaw Nadon aboard the *Tafanda Bay*. You must choose wisely. . . ."

"Listen," Solo said to the Oracle. "I can smuggle your Rebel leader aboard the *Tafanda Bay*, but that's not all I'm after —"

"Of course not," the Oracle said. "You want the Hutt child. You believe that it can save you."

Solo raised an eyebrow at the pale Ithorian. None of them had mentioned the Hutt in the Oracle's presence.

The Oracle nodded, closing his blind eyes. "The child is

aboard the herd ship, of course. In the old state room where Momaw Nadon housed the first representatives of the Empire. The bounty hunters await you. With the help of Momaw Nadon, you can find the child."

That night aboard the *Tafanda Bay*, General Dewes was eating dinner with his guests: Dengar (who had once saved his life), Udin, and Eron Stonefield.

An aide entered the room. "Sir, a message from the fleet. A ship just exited hyperspace — a diplomatic vessel, carrying the Torturer, Sir Vengnar Heiff."

"You're sure it's him this time?" the general asked.

"Positive," the aide said.

The general folded his hands on the dinner table, considering. "Most odd," he said to his guests. "First we get a message that the Torturer has come, and moments later learn that he was most likely killed in a deadly crash. However, no evidence of a crash is found. Now we find that the Torturer is only arriving."

"Of course," Dengar said, "I'm sure the first ship belonged to Han Solo. He's here on Ithor. It's time to collect our bounty."

"Indeed, I believe you're right," the general said. "Now all you have to do is find him."

Dengar shook his head. "He'll come to us. Excuse us, General," he said as he and the other bounty hunters rose from their seats at the table. "We must go set a trap. We have some Rebels to trap . . . dead or alive."

MISSION
BRIEFING

Before you proceed, you must consult the Mission Guide for the rules of the STAR WARS MISSIONS. You must follow these rules at all times.

This is a Rebel mission.

The Rebel Alliance has ordered you to smuggle Momaw Nadon onto the Ithorian herdship *Tafanda Bay*, in the hopes that he can give his people the will to resist the Empire. In addition, you know that bounty hunters have taken Grubba the Hutt to the *Tafanda Bay*. You need to retrieve the child so he can be used to pay off Jabba.

You start the mission with your MP total from your previous Mission. (Or 1000 MP, if this is your first Mission.)

Choose your character. You may take up to three weapons.

You may use Power three times on this Mission.

May the Force be with you.

Your Mission:
Ithorian
Invasion

During the night, you sleep well-hidden in the jungle. The Oracle has picked a spot that he promises will remain free of danger until well past dawn.

You are not so sure. Several times during the night you are wakened by the sound of TIE fighters swooping low over the trees. Deep down, you know they are hunting for you.

At dawn, you find fruits that have fallen to the forest floor — odd gray fruits with delicious red meat. Only a few of them have fallen — just enough to feed your party. Strangely, the fruits appeared just on the edge of your camp.

With Momaw Nadon, you leave camp in the morning, walking south. The big Ithorian is tall, but his legs are no longer than yours, so you travel at a comfortable pace. You move cautiously through thick foliage, walking through deep moss, brushing away jungle plants that bar your way.

He leads you along a path thick with trees, and warns you, "I am not the Oracle. The jungle does not love me as much as it does him. We must take care."

"Of what?" you ask.

"Many beasts in the jungle are fierce. Some plants eat meat, too. Long ago, we struggled to make peace with such creatures. Even the shadow hunters were our friends. But some animals have forgotten us now. And none will recognize you as a friend."

"What do I watch out for?" you ask.

At that moment, you are walking beneath a tree with long hanging tendrils. You brush one aside, and it suddenly twists in your hand, grasping your arm. A second long creeper loops over your head, grasping you by the neck. Before you can wrench free, it pulls upward, lifting you off your feet.

"This one is called the hangman's tree," Momaw Nadon explains. Then he shouts at the tree, "Leave him alone! Is this any way to treat a friend?" Momaw Nadon rushes forward and lifts you a moment so that you can get a breath. Then he grabs a fallen limb. With it he rushes up to the trunk of the tree and bats fiercely against it.

You try to tell Momaw Nadon that the tree is strangling you, but you can't speak.

You must free yourself. You can fight the tree with a weapon, persuade the tree that you are a friend (with Power), or struggle for air while Momaw Nadon tries to convince the tree to let you go.

To combat the tree with your weapon: Add your weaponry# to your weapon's close-range# for your confront#. Roll the 6-dice to combat the hangman's tree.

> If your confront# is equal to or more than your roll#, add the difference +2 to your MP total. The tree drops you to the ground and won't bother you again. You may proceed.

> If your confront# is lower than your roll#, subtract the difference from your MP total and repeat this confront until you have blown the bark off of this hungry tree.

To persuade the tree to release you (using Power)*: Choose your Persuasion Power or your Hypnotism Power. You clear your mind and whisper to the tree that you are a friend.

Your charm# + your Jedi# + your Power's mid-resist# is your confront#. Roll the 6-dice.

> *If your confront# is equal to or more than your roll#,* add the difference +1 to your MP total. The tree loves you, and pats you on the head with its tendrils as if to beg for forgiveness.

> *If your confront# is lower than your roll#,* subtract the difference from your MP total. The tree doesn't trust you. You must struggle for breath until Momaw Nadon can save you (below).

*Note: This counts as one of three Power uses you are allowed on this Mission.

> **To struggle for breath until Momaw Nadon can release you:** Your skill# + your strength# is your confront#. Roll the 6-dice.

> *If your confront# is equal to or more than your roll#,* add the difference to your MP total. You gulp a breath of air, and Momaw Nadon quickly convinces the tree that you are a friend.

> *If your confront# is lower than your roll#,* subtract the difference from your MP total. Add +1 to your confront# for your new confront#. Repeat the confront using the new confront# until you are saved.

You massage the rope burns on your neck. The hangman's vine gave you a good stretch, and you wonder if you're a little taller now.

You and Momaw Nadon continue through the jungle, climbing toward the mountains. Near noon, you come out of the jungle into the hills. The hillsides are covered with enormous vines that hold giant green forrolow berries, each almost the length of a man. The berries lay on the ground, ripening like melons. You can smell their sweet scent, like syrup covering the hillside. The sun is warm on your face.

In the distance, near the tops of the hills, you can see the *Tafanda Bay* floating toward you. You identify its gleaming domes, wide gardens, and ornate towers. The top half provides the living quarters for hundreds of thousands of Ithorians. The bottom half is equipped with engine rooms and ship's bays. A steady stream of small leaf ships trails out on the horizon, flying toward the *Tafanda Bay*.

At the very lowest level of the ship are long hairlike tentacles reaching toward the ground. As these skim the treetops, sometimes a tentacle will pull upward, carrying something into the ship.

"Those are the harvesting tentacles," Momaw Nadon explains. "Our city never lands, but we harvest what we need when it skims low over the ground. A computer on the ship tells the tentacles what to harvest and when. If we hold onto a berry, the tentacles will lift us into the food processor."

You gauge the direction of the ship, and try to plan an intercept course.

Behind you, a deep voice shouts, "Hey, what are you two doing here?"

You turn.

Two stormtroopers stand at the edge of the woods, cradling their weapons a hundred yards off. Behind them is a landspeeder.

You can fight the stormtroopers, lie to them, or evade them.

To fight the stormtroopers: Choose your weapon. Add your weaponry# to your weapon's mid-range# for your confront#. Roll the 6-dice to combat each stormtrooper in turn.

> *If your confront# is equal to or more than your roll#,* add the difference +3 to your MP total, you have defeated the first stormtrooper. Proceed to combat the second stormtrooper, using the same confront equation. Once you have defeated both stormtroopers, you may take their landspeeder.

> *If your confront# is lower than your roll#,* subtract the difference from your MP total. Add +1 to your confront# for you new confront#. Continue the confront, using the new confront#, until you defeat both stormtroopers.

To lie (without Power): You tell the stormtroopers that you are an Imperial scientist, sent to study forrolow berry populations. You ask if you can borrow their speeder, to take a sample berry to the *Tafanda Bay,* and you promise to return it. Your charm# +3 is your confront#. Roll the 12-dice to deceive the stormtroopers.

> *If your confront# is equal to or more than your roll#,* add the difference +10 to your MP total. The stormtroopers believe you, and offer the use of their speeder.

If your confront# is lower than your roll#, subtract the difference from your MP total. The guards don't believe you, and you must either fight (above) or evade (below).

To lie (with Power)*: Choose your Persuasion Power or your Deception Power. You tell the stormtroopers that you are scientists studying the berries, and that you would like to use their landspeeder to take a sample to the *Tafanda Bay.* Your charm# + your Power's mid-resist# + your Jedi# is your confront#. Roll the 6-dice to deceive the guards.

If your confront# is equal to or more than your roll#, add the difference +8 to your MP total. The guards lend you their speeder.

If your confront# is lower than your roll#, subtract the difference from your MP total. The guards don't believe you. "Shoot him!" the leader shouts. You must fight (above) or evade (below).

*Note: This counts as one of three Power uses you are allowed on this Mission.

To evade the stormtroopers (without Power): You and Momaw Nadon run into the trees. Your stealth# + your skill# +3 is your confront#. Roll the 12-dice to evade the stormtroopers.

If your confront# is equal to or more than your roll#, add the difference +10 to your MP total. The stormtroopers quickly lose sight of you in the trees. While they chase you, you race to their landspeeder.

If your confront# is lower than your roll#, subtract the difference from your MP total. The stormtroopers shoot blindly at you in the trees. Add +1 to your confront# and repeat the confront until you evade the troopers.

To evade the stormtroopers (with Power)*: Choose your Evasion Power or your Camouflage Power. You and Momaw Nadon run into the trees. Your Jedi# + your Power's low-resist# + your stealth# is your confront#. Roll the 6-dice to evade the stormtroopers.

If your confront# is equal to or more than your roll#, add the difference +9 to your MP total. The stormtroopers quickly lose sight of you in the trees. While they chase you, you hop into their landspeeder.

If your confront# is lower than your roll#, subtract the difference from your MP total. The stormtroopers shoot blindly at you in the trees. Repeat the confront until you evade them completely.

*Note: This counts as one of three Power uses you are allowed on this Mission.

You have defeated both troopers and gained a landspeeder. Reward yourself with 15MP (30MP for Advanced Level players).

You and Momaw Nadon take the landspeeder and fly over the hills until you near the *Tafanda Bay.* The enormous ship is heading right toward you. The sound of its giant repulsor-lift engines shakes the earth.

Thousands of enormous tentacles reach down beneath the ship. They are copper-colored, yet remind you painfully of the vines from the hangman's tree.

The tendrils grasp giant forrolow berries, then tenderly pluck them and carry them up to the ship.

Momaw Nadon rushes to a giant fruit and grabs onto its stem. "Here," he shouts. "Hold on, like this."

You grasp a berry. He shouts, "Not that — a ripe one."

The one you have is not as deep a green as his, so you go to a nearby vine.

The ship flies over you, and suddenly the great copper tentacles dangle all around you.

One grasps your berry, and lifts it into the air.

To hang onto the giant berry: Your strength# +1 is your confront#. Roll the 6-dice.

> *If your confront# is equal to or more than your roll#,* add the difference +5 to your MP total. You kick your feet out and swing wildly, enjoying the easy ride up.

> *If your confront# is lower than your roll#,* subtract the difference from your MP total. You hang on for dear life and must pull yourself to a more stable position. Repeat the confront until you successfully hang on.

The tentacle lifts you higher and higher, a hundred yards in the air, until it pulls you through a large hole, into the *Tafanda Bay*. There are no overhead lights here, only the light shining up through the floors. There is a tremendous noise of engines whirring, and the clank of metal as the giant tentacles work.

Momaw Nadon shouts. He is being carried toward a huge hopper. The hopper has wheels that let it roll along a track. The tentacle drops him and his berry into the hopper. Momaw Nadon tries to get up, but immediately another tentacle drops a huge green fruit on him. The forrolow berry knocks Momaw Nadon down. Other fruits quickly pile on him. You have to save him!

Your own tentacle whips you toward the hopper, and you land into the green fruit with a splat. Momaw Nadon is somewhere beneath you. You have to dig him out.

To dig Momaw Nadon out: Your skill# +2 is your conflict#. Roll the 6-dice.

> *If your confront# is equal to or more than your roll#,* add the difference to your MP total. You plunge your hand down until you feel Momaw Nadon, and then slide him up through the oozing berries.

> *If your confront# is lower than your roll#,* subtract the difference from your MP total. Repeat this confront until you find Momaw Nadon.

The hopper of berries begins whirring down a track.

Weakly, Momaw Nadon says, "We must get out of this vessel at once. We don't want to get dumped into the cookers."

Ahead, along the track, you see a light. There is a machine up there, with an entrance like an enormous tunnel. Steam belches from the entrance. Above it is an observation platform equipped with an enormous spotlight that shines down on the rolling hoppers of berries. Two stormtroopers with heavy blasters stand next to the light, suspiciously studying the contents of each shipment and guarding a large door.

"Quickly," Momaw Nadon hisses. "Jump before we reach their light."

You look over the side of the vehicle. It is moving very fast — this isn't going to be easy. You leap from the fruit hopper to the tracks.

Up above, one of the stormtroopers shouts, "Hey, I'm pretty sure I saw something down there. Help me aim this light better."

He reaches up to pull a lever.

You realize that the only way out of the hold is to climb the ladder that leads to the guards. You can't simply evade them. But the spotlight they are using runs an electric current through a container of gas that is under high pressure. If you shoot the light, it will explode!

To shoot the light: Choose your weapon. Add your weaponry# to your weapon's far-range# +4 for your confront#. Roll the 12-dice.

If your confront# is equal to or more than your roll#, add the difference +3 to your MP total. It's a perfect hit. The light explodes, throwing both stormtroopers from the platform. You may now proceed.

If your confront# is lower than your roll#, subtract the difference from your MP total. The stormtroopers are on to you! Subtract +1 from your confront# for your new

confront#. Repeat this confront with your new con-
front# until you hit the light.

You run to the ladder that leads to the observation platform where the guards were posted.

Momaw Nadon looks down at the fallen stormtroopers
thoughtfully. "I wonder why guards are here at all. Do you
think they were expecting us?"

"It's doubtful," you say.

At that moment, you hear a dull noise from one of the
stormtrooper's helmets. A tinny voice says, "Station 114,
this is Control. We have a report of possible blaster fire in
your area. Report in. Check."

You fumble for the helmet. If these dead guards don't
report in, someone will come looking for them.

You can lie to the control officer without Power, or you
can lie to him with Power.

To lie (without Power): You tell control that you shot at a
giant bossuk roach that you saw among the berries. Your
charm# +1 is your confront#. Roll the 6-dice.

If your confront# is equal to or more than your roll#, add
the difference +5 to your MP total. The control officer
tells you, "Okay, but keep it down to a dull roar."

If your confront# is lower than your roll#, subtract 4MP
from your MP total. The control officer shouts at you,
"You know its against the regs to discharge your
firearms without authorization. Next time, let the bugs
go." You offer lame apologies. Add +1 to your con-

front# for your new confront#. Repeat the confront with your new confront# until you have satisfied the control officer.

To lie (using Power)*: Choose your Persuasion Power or Deception Power. You tell the control officer that a giant bossuk roach attacked you. Your Jedi# + your Power's low-resist# + your charm# is your confront#. Roll the 6-dice.

If your confront# is equal to or more than your roll#, add the difference +5 to your MP total. "All right," the control officer says. "I hate them roaches."

If your confront# is lower than your roll#, subtract the difference from your MP total. The control officer is in a terrible mood, and screams that he never did like you in the first place, and now you are only proving that you can't do anything right. Now you must offer apologies. Repeat this confront until you succeed.

*Note: This counts as one of three Power uses you are allowed on this Mission.

"Roger," the control officer says when he's done. "We have a hammerhead security team on the way. We don't want another infestation of *those* things."

"Quickly," Momaw Nadon tells you, "we must go."

He leads you through the door that the stormtroopers were guarding. It opens into a corridor that overlooks much of the giant machinery. You see the berries down below, dumped from their hoppers onto a sorting rack. On the rack, sprayers hose the berries off with steaming water, and then mechanical arms pluck off the stems.

Afterward, the stems are thrown into a mulching machine to fertilize the forest floor, while the berries go into a huge vat.

Ahead, a catwalk leads over the top of the berry vats.

You look up. Three Ithorians wearing security uniforms are walking toward you. They hold blaster rifles. One of them looks up and sees Momaw Nadon.

"You!" he shouts accusingly. "What are you doing back here?"

Momaw Nadon steps forward. "I have heard that my people suffer. That the trees below us suffer. That our whole world lies in pain. It is time for us to end this. We must throw off our Imperial shackles."

The Ithorian raises his weapon, as if to threaten Momaw Nadon. "Those words are treason against the Empire."

Momaw Nadon steps back in shock. "Are you part of the Empire now, Boma Inondo?" he asks. "Do you raise your weapon against your *own* people?"

Boma Inondo growls and steps forward menacingly, "You are not *my* people! You were exiled!"

"Yes," Momaw Nadon answers. "I was exiled for suggesting that we should fight the Empire. Certainly, by now, you must know that I was right. Will you use your gun against *me*, or against the Empire?"

Boma Inondo is shaking with fear. Behind him, an Ithorian says, "The Empire has offered a reward for Momaw Nadon."

Momaw Nadon scowls. "You were my Chief of Security, Boma. Do you want to remain a prisoner of the Empire?"

Boma Inondo raises his weapon. "We are not prisoners," he says. "We are the Empire's trustees."

Both of Momaw Nadon's mouths fall open as he stares in shock. He cannot believe that one of his own people now serves the Empire. You suspect that these three Ithorians can't be trusted, though they really don't seem to want to shoot their old leader. Even when serving the Empire, Ithorians hate violence.

"I'm going to call Imperial security," Boma Inondo says. He reaches for a communicator.

You rush him.

Boma Inondo swings his gun, attempting to knock you off the catwalk. You pivot, grabbing his weapon. You struggle as he tries, with his great strength, to toss you into the berry vat.

To combat the Ithorian hand-to-hand: Your strength# + your skill# + your stealth# +1 is your confront#. Roll the 12-dice.

If your confront# is equal to or more than your roll#, add the difference +2 to your MP total. You trip Boma Inondo, tossing him into the berries.

If your confront# is lower than your roll#, subtract the difference from your MP total. Add +1 to your confront# for your new confront#. Repeat this confront using the same new confront# until you defeat Boma Inondo.

Boma Inondo is hurled into the berries with a loud splat. Green ooze goes flying. The other two Ithorian security guards stagger back, shocked by this display of violence.

Down in the vat, Boma is covered with green berry slime. He wipes some off his face and cries, "I hate you, Momaw Nadon!"

Momaw waves a hand at the berry vat and laughs. "Now you can taste the fruits of your own anger. Berry your hatred, before it *berries* you."

"The only thing I hate more than puns," Boma says, "are the people who make them."

He raises his blaster to fire, but berries have plugged its barrel. The blaster rifle explodes in his hands. Boma sinks into the vat of green goo, as it rolls toward the ovens.

"Remind me not to eat any pies tomorrow," you tell Momaw Nadon.

You raise your blaster and point at the other two Ithorians. "Your boss didn't make a *berry* good Imperial agent, but he'll make a fine fruit filling. Do you want to join him?"

You know that you're not here to fight the Ithorians. Before you go on, you must try to persuade them to join you.

To persuade the Ithorians (without Power): You say, "Come on, I don't want to have to use this any more than you do." Your charm# +1 is your confront#. Roll the 6-dice.

> *If your confront# is equal to or more than your roll#,* add the difference to your MP total. You have won the hearts of the security guards. You may now proceed.

If your confront# is lower than your roll#, subtract the difference from your MP total. The Ithorians are not convinced. You decide to threaten them (below).

To persuade the Ithorian guards (using Power)*: You must use your Persuasion Power. Your charm# + your Jedi# + your Power's high-resist# is your confront#. Roll the 6-dice.

If your confront# is equal to or more than your roll#, add 10 MP to your MP total. The guards would willingly follow you anywhere.

If your confront# is lower than your roll#, subtract the difference from your MP total. The Ithorians are not persuaded. You must threaten them (below).

*Note: This counts as one of three Power uses you are allowed on this Mission.

To threaten the Ithorian guards: Choose your weapon. You aim and fire at a nearby fruit. Your weaponry# + your weapon's mid-range# +1 is your confront#. Roll the 6-dice.

If your confront# is equal to or more than your roll#, add the difference to your MP total. The fruit is demolished. You growl, "You're next," to the guards. They are fully intimidated.

If your confront# is lower than your roll#, subtract the difference from your MP total. You miss. The guards are not fully threatened. It will be up to Momaw Nadon to persuade them.

Momaw Nadon says to the two security guards, "In the past you have used your weapons to hunt down vermin. Now, you will hunt Imperial vermin. Tell me, what have the Imperials been doing on our ships?"

One guard lowers his head, as if these words make him sad to speak. "You were right when you said that we should never have surrendered to the Empire. They have taken our proudest city. They study the way that we build our ships from leaves and glue, and dream of forming new types of armor. They see what our doctors have done, and instead of learning about new medicines, they want to learn about natural poisons."

The other one pipes in, his deep voice issuing from twin mouths. "They rob us. They tried to steal the knowledge we would freely have given, and now they torture our scientists, seeking to learn that which few should know."

You say that you have heard that Sir Vengnar Heiff is on the *Tafanda Bay*.

"Yes," one security guard confirms. "You can hear the cries in the prison hold. Even General Dewes is appalled."

Momaw Nadon says in shock, "Prison hold? We have no prison!"

"Levels seven through nine are the prison holds," the guard reports.

"But — those were *nurseries* when I was here." Momaw Nadon crosses his arms, deep in thought. "General Dewes lied to me at every turn. He said that he was transporting in aides to help us in our work, and instead he sent spies. He said he was sending in technicians, and he sent in troops. He said that if we revealed our secrets, he would withdraw his scientists from our jungles, and instead he pillages our land. Now he turns our home into a prison. I cannot believe that there is any limit to his evil."

You remember the words of the Oracle: "Not everyone who wears an Imperial uniform is wholly given to evil." Perhaps he meant Dewes. "Lying to a people and plundering their land is one thing," you say. "Torture and murder is another. Perhaps this Dewes could be turned into an ally."

"Surely you don't believe that," Momaw Nadon says. He studies you from narrow eyes. "He blinded the Oracle and threw him from the ship in an effort to kill him."

"If Dewes had wanted the Oracle dead, there are surer ways to have done it," you point out. "For an Imperial goon, this one sounds pretty squeamish."

Momaw Nadon trembles at your words, as if in a subdued rage. "He took everything from me: my pride, my home, my family, my people."

"He left you with your life," you point out.

"He is a weed that must be plucked out," Momaw Nadon says with finality.

You squint at Momaw Nadon in turn, wondering what is in his heart.

After a brief discussion with the security guards, you discover that there are not really many Imperials on the *Tafanda Bay*. The Ithorians never needed weapons, and even when beaten and enslaved have never raised a hand against their captors.

A few stormtroopers guard a number of key areas of the ship — the entrances and exits, and the control centers.

You figure that with a few good men, you can handle most of them yourself.

"Show me where to go," you tell the Ithorians. You ask them about Grubba the Hutt, but they have no idea where he might be — or if, indeed, he is on the ship.

Momaw Nadon says, "We need weapons. We must raid their armory."

This sounds like a good plan. It will keep the Imperials from retrieving the weapons and it lets you arm the Ithorians at the same time.

The security guards lead you to the armory in an industrial section of the *Tafanda Bay*, in an old warehouse. What you see there freezes your heart.

The outside of the warehouse is guarded by an IG-88 assassin droid. The door to the warehouse is open, and inside you see stormtroopers. You can also see part of the arsenal inside — a portable ion cannon, rows of detonators, and heavy blasters. You can't shoot into that arsenal. One stray blaster bolt would blow up the whole city.

You might have to fight them hand-to-hand, even though the stormtroopers are wearing armor. But you certainly can't fight an assassin droid that way.

You study the Ithorian security guards. Both of them have blasters. Still, just moments ago they couldn't work up the nerve to shoot at you. You ask them quietly if they've ever shot at anything besides bugs and rats.

They both shake their heads no.

"Think you can take out that assassin droid?" you ask. "It's not like its a living organism."

"I have shot at aluminum beverage containers," one Ithorian guard answers. "This would be little different."

"Yeah, but those aluminum beverage containers weren't

shooting back," you warn. "This time, their big brother just might get even."

The guards insist they can kill the droid.

"Good," you tell them. "Escort me to the warehouse. I'll try to distract the guards inside. You open up on that killer droid. And be careful. I don't want to get caught in your crossfire. Momaw Nadon will back me up."

You see a large metal hammer sitting beside a workbench, and casually tuck it behind your back, down your belt.

The Ithorian guards escort you to the armory. They both seem very nervous. You wonder if you can really trust them.

When you are twenty feet from the door of the armory, the IG-88 assassin droid calls, "Halt!"

You all stop.

"What is your purpose?" the droid asks.

"My name is Troy," you say. "I am a counselor to Sir Vengnar Heiff, who is here on a diplomatic mission. He asked me to get a few things from the armory."

"What things?" the assassin droid asks. "Where are your requisition forms?"

The two stormtroopers have now stopped what they are doing in order to back up the droid. You may try to deceive them without Power, or with Power.

To deceive (without Power): Your charm# +1 is your confront#. You promise to bring by the requisition forms as soon as you're done. Roll the 6-dice to lie to the stormtroopers.

If your confront# is equal to or more than your roll#, add 10MP to your MP total. The stormtroopers and the droid believe you, and are willing to help.

If your confront# is lower than your roll#, subtract 10MP from your MP total. The guards remain skeptical but curious.

To lie (with Power)*: Choose your Persuasion Power or your Deception Power. Your Power's mid-resist# + your Jedi# is your confront#. Roll the 6-dice to deceive the guards.

If your confront# is equal to or more than your roll#, add 10MP to your MP total. The guards usher you forward.

If your confront# is lower than your roll#, subtract 10MP from your MP total. The guards remain cautious, yet are willing to let you proceed.

*Note: This counts as one of three Power uses you are allowed on this Mission.

The stormtroopers laugh. "Sure, we can equip you. Say, it's good to see another human face around here. What planet you from?"

"Bop-Me," you answer as you walk up to the guards. The IG-88 assassin droid is only inches from you.

"Bop-Me?" the stormtrooper asks, confused.

"Okay," you say, "if you insist." You pull your hammer from behind your back, just as the Ithorian security guards swing their blasters around and fire on the droid.

To combat the first guard: Add your strength# to your skill# for your confront#. Roll the 6-dice.

If your confront# is equal to or more than your roll#, add the difference to your MP total. You land a good solid blow that will keep this guy dreaming all night. You may proceed.

If your confront# is lower than your roll#, subtract the difference from your MP total. Add +1 to your confront# for your new confront#. Repeat this confront using the new confront# until you defeat the guard.

The Ithorian guards fire on IG-88. The first shot glances harmlessly from its armored body. It fires on its attacker, and the Ithorian is blown backward. The second Ithorian fires almost instantly, catching the droid at the base of its metallic head. The body breaks open with explosive force.

To dodge the pieces of exploding droid: Your skill# +2 is your confront#. Roll the 6-dice.

If your confront# is equal to or more than your roll#, add the difference +4 to your MP total. You've got the instincts of a Wookiee. You may proceed.

If your confront# is lower than your roll#, subtract the difference from your MP total. It really stings when shrapnel gets lodged in your shooting arm. Subtract +1 from your weaponry# for the rest of this Mission.

You turn your attention back to the last guard. He's scurrying toward a rack of assault rifles. He shouts into his comlink, "Security breach in the armory!"

You may fight the guard hand-to-hand, persuade him to surrender with Power, or persuade without Power. You *cannot* shoot, because any stray fire could blow up the armory — and the ship.

To persuade the stormtrooper (without Power): You say, "Give it up. You're outnumbered, and if you try firing weapons in here, we're all going to blow." Your charm# +1 is your confront#. Roll the 6-dice.

If your confront# is equal to or more than your roll#, add the difference +5 to your MP total. This guy didn't really want to die. You may now proceed.

If your confront# is lower than your roll#, subtract the difference from your MP total. The guy grabs a gun. You'll have to fight (below).

To persuade the stormtrooper (using Power)*: You must use your Persuasion Power. Your charm# + your Jedi# + your Power's low-resist# is your confront#. Roll the 6-dice.

If your confront# is equal to or more than your roll#, add the difference +5 to your MP total. The guard thanks you for sparing him. You may now proceed.

If your confront# is lower than your roll#, subtract the difference from your MP total. The guard sneers at you as he grasps a gun. "I don't care if we all die!" he shouts.

"I've been looking for a way out of this lowlife outfit!" You must fight him (below).

Note: This counts as one of three Power uses you are allowed on this Mission.

To combat the stormtrooper: Add your strength# to your skill# for your confront#. Roll the 6-dice.

If your confront# is equal to or more than your roll#, add the difference to your MP total. As you whack him with the hammer, you shout, "You know, the Empire gives medals for wounds like that." You may proceed.

If your confront# is lower than your roll#, subtract the difference from your MP total. The guard grabs a blaster rifle and swings at you, trying to club you with the stock of the gun. Add +1 to your confront# for your new confront#. Repeat this confront using the new confront# until you defeat the guard.

Nice work! Reward yourself with 55MP (80MP for Advanced Level players).

The sound of combat draws attention. Dozens of curious Ithorians rush down the halls. One shouts, "It's Momaw Nadon! He has returned!" Many Ithorians bow, as if to a revered king. Their eye stalks nearly sweep the floor.

"What do you want of us?" an Ithorian asks Momaw Nadon. You glance at him. He is a poor creature, wearing rags for robes.

"The weeds choke our garden," Momaw Nadon answers. "It is time to pluck them out."

Behind Momaw Nadon, another Ithorian shouts, "Long live the Gardener! Down with the Empire!" He salutes.

Suddenly, dozens of Ithorians begin to shout and rush into the armory, inflamed by the idea of rebellion. They grab assault rifles and armored riot shields.

Momaw Nadon looks at you as they do so, and he says softly, "My people need a leader who knows how to fight. You must show them the way."

The Ithorians rush out of the armory, bearing weapons. One of them tosses you a shield — good protection when you're running down a hall toward armed foes.

"To the command center!" one Ithorian shouts, and he rushes down a corridor. Several Ithorians follow him.

You chase after them, over an access bridge and up a hallway. Everywhere that you and your cohorts run, you see Ithorians by the score. They all begin to shout excitedly and raise their fists into the air.

You sprint toward the command center, and suddenly there is an explosion ahead. The Ithorian in front of you is cut down by blaster fire. Ahead and behind you, Ithorians and stormtroopers exchange fire.

You raise your shield. The corridor fills with smoke from the weapons. You fire blindly and rush forward. A blaster bolt shoots overhead, and you duck to the floor.

Ahead, dimly, you see where stormtroopers have thrown some chairs down into the hall as a barricade.

One of them spots you.

To fight the stormtrooper: Choose your weapon. Add your weaponry# to your weapon's mid-range# for your confront#. Roll the 6-dice.

If your confront# is equal to or more than your roll#, add the difference to your MP total. It's a perfect hit. You may now proceed.

If your confront# is lower than your roll#, subtract the difference from your MP total. Add +1 to your confront# for your new confront#. Repeat the confront using the new confront# until you succeed.

Through the cover of the smoke, you rush toward the barricade. Other stormtroopers are wisely keeping their heads down. You want to get as close as possible.

To avoid being spotted: Your stealth# +1 is your confront#. Roll the 6-dice.

If your confront# is equal to or more than your roll#, add the difference +7 to your MP total. You quietly crawl through the smoke. You may now proceed.

If your confront# is lower than your roll#, subtract the difference from your MP total. A stormtrooper spots you and shouts a warning, then jumps up to take aim. You must fight (below).

To fight the stormtrooper: Add your weaponry# to your weapon's close-range# for your confront#. Roll the 6-dice.

If your confront# is equal to or more than your roll#, add the difference to your MP total. There's one stormtrooper who won't ever collect his retirement benefits. You may proceed.

If your confront# is lower than your roll#, subtract the difference from your MP total. Add +1 to your confront# for your new confront#. Repeat the confront using the new confront# until the stormtrooper is just an unpleasant memory.

Blaster fire whips ferociously overhead. The Ithorians behind you are aiming high. You hope its because they know where you are. A thermal detonator comes rolling through the smoke toward you. You see that its red arming light is on. It's going to explode!

To grab the detonator and lob it over the barricade into the midst of the stormtroopers: Add your strength# to your skill# +4 for your confront#. Roll the 12-dice.

If your confront# is equal to or more than your roll#, add the difference +4 to your MP total. The bomb lofts gently over the barricade. You may now proceed.

If your confront# is lower than your roll#, subtract the difference from your MP total. Try again — *quickly!* Repeat this confront with the same confront# until you succeed.

Body armor flies everywhere. But two more stormtroopers are rushing at you through the smoke!

You raise your weapon and fire, but find that you're out of ammo.

To reload under fire: Your skill# +1 is your confront#. Roll the 6-dice.

> *If your confront# is equal to or more than your roll#,* add the difference to your MP total. The new ammo slips in easily. You may now proceed.

> *If your confront# is lower than your roll#,* subtract 3 MP from your MP total. Add +1 to your confront# to get your new confront#. Repeat the confront until you have reloaded the weapon.

Fortunately, the Ithorians keep shooting over your head while you reload. Now it's time for action! You decide to rush these guys, before they can get under cover.

To kick down the barricade and battle the stormtroopers: Your weaponry# + your weapon's short-range# + your skill# + your strength# is your confront#. Roll the 12-dice.

> *If your confront# is equal to or more than your roll#,* add the difference +7 to your MP total. You're so good, you make these heroics look easy. You may proceed.

> *If your confront# is lower than your roll#,* subtract the difference from your MP total. Add +1 to your confront# for your new confront#. Repeat the confront using the new confront# until you succeed.

For making it this far alive, add 40MP to your MP total (60MP for Advanced Level players).

You rush into the command center with the Ithorians right behind you. A dozen Imperial workers are at various monitoring stations.

General Dewes, looking regal in his dark uniform, shouts to one of his men, "Captain, warn the fleet that we are under attack." At the same moment, a lieutenant raises a sleek blaster and takes aim at you, as if you two were engaged in a gentlemanly duel.

But you must stop these men from warning the fleet at all costs! The Star Destroyers overhead could blow the *Tafanda Bay* to pieces.

You decide to disable the communications console, while diving away from your attacker.

You may disable the console with Power, smash the console with your strength, or shoot the console.

To disable the communications console (with Power)*: Choose your Object Movement Power. Your Jedi# + your Power's low-resist# + your skill# +2 is your confront#. Roll the 12-dice.

If your confront# is equal to or more than your roll#, add the difference +3 to your MP total. The console is disabled. You may now proceed.

If your confront# is lower than your roll#, subtract the difference from your MP total. You must either smash the thing with your fists, or shoot it (below).

*Note: This counts as one of three Power uses you are allowed on this Mission.

To destroy the console with your fists: Add your strength# to your stealth# for your confront#. Roll the 6-dice.

> *If your confront# is equal to or more than your roll#,* add the difference +4 to your MP total. You leap forward and slam your fist into the console. Sparks fly everywhere, but on a day like today, you feel lightning-proof. You may now proceed.

> *If your confront# is lower than your roll#,* subtract the difference from your MP total. Repeat the confront until you succeed.

To destroy the communications console with your weapon: Add your weaponry# to your weapon's close-range# for your confront#. Roll the 6-dice.

> *If your confront# is equal to or more than your roll#,* add the difference +4 to your MP total. You hit the bull's-eye and may proceed.

> *If your confront# is lower than your roll#,* subtract the difference from your MP total. Repeat the confront until you succeed.

The console can never be repaired.

As you roll back to your feet, a dozen Ithorians rush into the room, bristling with weapons. The gun-happy lieutenant gets vaporized, and terrified General Dewes stands, looking pale.

Momaw Nadon enters the command center. He says coldly, "General Dewes, years ago I invited you here as an Imperial observer, to learn our ways, and to prosper from our medicines. You abused my hospitality. It is now time for the Empire to leave."

General Dewes trembles, and shakes his head no. "I am a soldier under the Emperor's command. I cannot simply order the fleets away."

Momaw Nadon stalks toward the general, hands clenched into fists. You hand Momaw Nadon a blaster.

Momaw Nadon raises it to the general's chest. At that moment, in the utter silence, you hear voices — thousands of Ithorian voices shouting in triumph. At that moment, at least, the *Tafanda Bay* is free. Mingled among those shouts, you hear gunfire. The Ithorians are defeating Imperial stormtroopers all over the ship.

You look up at a monitor and see a ship blasting out of one of the docking bays. A nearby Ithorian dives for a console and tries to lock a tractor beam on the fleeing ship. But he's not familiar with the systems, and the ship gets away.

Momaw Nadon tells his people, "Lock down the city. I won't have any more Imperials escaping. And get these prisoners to their cells."

You glance up at a clock in the command center. It reads noon. The Rebels had promised to clear away Imperial Star Destroyers by noon.

You look to a monitor aboard that station, which shows

the vessels in the sky overhead. You can still see the big blips of the Imperial Star Destroyers, but suddenly the screen goes white with hundreds of other blips, as Rebel ships drop out of hyperspace. You are tempted to stay and watch the engagement.

"Sir," you say to Momaw Nadon. "I have business elsewhere."

First, you must capture the Torturer. Then you will have time to find Grubba.

You hear heavy gunfire coming from elevator shafts above. Momaw Nadon says, "I fear we all do."

You rush down the hall to the hydrolift and jump in. Three Ithorians follow you. You press the button for Level 8. You have been told that is where the Torturer should be.

The hydrolift whirs and carries you upward.

It stops at Level 8, opening wide. You hear the cries of hundreds of Ithorian prisoners, still locked in their cells. The door opens into a room similar to the command center. Six long halls lead out from this room, which is crammed with locking mechanisms and monitors for watching the prison. The room is filled with smoke. A dozen dead Ithorians lay on the floor, and in the center of the room, standing over the bodies, you see three stormtroopers. At their center you see an alien, a lizard man with forest-green scales and a ridge of horns that spread out from his eyes. He wears only a utility belt and a brilliant red cape that identifies him as an Imperial torturer. His excruciatingly long claws are dripping with Ithorian blood. This must be Sir Heiff.

The stormtroopers whirl toward you. You raise your

weapon to fire into their ranks, then decide your forces would do better if you spread out and don't present a single target. You dive behind a console and fire.

To shoot the first stormtrooper: Add your weaponry# to your weapon's mid-range# +4 for your confront#. Roll the 12-dice.

If your confront# is equal to or more than your roll#, add the difference +5 to your MP total. It's a perfect shot. You may now proceed.

If your confront# is lower than your roll#, subtract the difference from your MP total. Add +2 to your confront# to get your new confront#. Repeat the confront using the new confront# until you succeed.

The Ithorians are poor fighters. They stand in the elevator, shooting as fast as they can. Some of their shots are wild, and only one other stormtrooper goes down before the Ithorians are defeated.

You glance up, looking for Sir Heiff and the other stormtroopers, but both of them have taken cover and you can't see them.

Suddenly, the lights in the room go off. You hear an evil laugh from Sir Heiff.

"Welcome to your nightmare," he says in a deep, rasping voice. "In the icy forests of my home world, I would often hunt at night. You see, I am blinded now, like you are. But I can smell your sweat, your blood, your fear."

You know that Heiff and the stormtroopers know

where you are hiding. You scramble back in the darkness, listening intently.

Suddenly, off to your left, you hear the gentle clack of a stormtrooper's battle armor as he sneaks toward you. Your back leg rubs up against a weapon on the floor. You pick it up, and toss it toward the stormtrooper.

The weapon hits the floor with a clatter, and the trooper whirls and fires. You see the flash of his blaster muzzle in the darkness.

To shoot the stormtrooper: Choose your weapon. Add your weaponry# to your weapon's close-range# for your confront#. Roll the 6-dice.

> *If your confront# is equal to or more than your roll#,* add the difference +7 to your MP total. It's a perfect shot. You may now proceed.

> *If your confront# is lower than your roll#,* subtract the difference from your MP total. Add +1 to your confront# to get your new confront#. Repeat the confront with your new confront# until you succeed.

The stormtrooper goes down with a scream. At that moment, something enormous lands atop you. Claws rip into your arm.

Sir Heiff!

The alien struggles to rip your weapon from your grasp.

To retain your weapon: Add your strength# to your stealth# for your confront#. Roll the 6-dice.

If your confront# is equal to or more than your roll#, add the difference +5 to your MP total. You elude Sir Heiff with your weapon intact. You may now proceed.

If your confront# is lower than your roll#, subtract 7MP from your MP total. The weapon clatters away in the darkness. Choose one of your backup weapons to use for the remainder of this Mission.

After pushing the monster backward you roll to the floor. You shoot blindly in his direction, but in your own muzzle flash, you can no longer see the red-cloaked beast.

In the corridors, on the prison block, Ithorians plead to you, "Open the cells, let us out."

You back up in the dark and stumble against a console. It has a heavy lever on it that will open the cell doors. "Maybe you can hunt me with tooth and claw," you tell Heiff. "But you can't stop all of us."

You pull the lever. A heavy mechanical thud tells you that the bolts have opened on the locks.

Sir Heiff snarls in the darkness. You fire in his general direction, and though you miss, in the muzzle flash you see him leaping toward you.

You duck and fire.

Heiff lands beside you and bounds away.

You suddenly hear a hydrolift door hiss closed. You run toward it, fearing the Heiff has escaped.

Then you hear a sharp intake of breath, just ahead. It was a trick! He's getting ready to attack.

You raise your shield to block his blow.

To block the blow: Add your skill# to your stealth# for your confront#. Roll the 6-dice.

> *If your confront# is equal to or more than your roll#,* add the difference +5 to your MP total. Sir Heiff's bloody claws leave a trail across your shield. You may now proceed.

> *If your confront# is lower than your roll#,* subtract 8MP from your MP total. The shield is knocked back into your face, stunning you momentarily.

Now that you know where he is, you raise your weapon and fire.

To shoot the Torturer: Your weaponry# + your weapon's close-range# +3 is your confront#. Roll the 12-dice.

> *If your confront# is equal to or more than your roll#,* add the difference +10 to your MP total. You've hit him! You may now proceed.

> *If your confront# is lower than your roll#,* subtract the difference from your MP total. You missed, but you located Sir Heiff more clearly in the muzzle flash. Add +2 to your confront# to get your new confront#. Repeat the confront with this new confront# until you succeed.

Add 30MP to your MP total for defeating Sir Heiff (45MP for Advanced Level players).

The Ithorians rush out from their cells and fill the room. One of them turns on the lights.

Sir Heiff is lying in a pool of blood as crimson as his torturer's robe. He is seriously injured.

"Finish me!" he shouts at you.

The stern Ithorians circle the Torturer.

You shake your head at Heiff's plea for a merciful death. "You have made your living torturing innocent people," you say. "I'll leave you to Ithorian justice. I suspect they'll treat you better than you deserve."

You turn away from Sir Heiff. He begins to sob in fear of what the Ithorians will do.

"Can some of you help me?" you ask the Ithorian prisoners. "I've got one last piece of business here. Take me to the state rooms, where you keep your visitors."

A dozen Ithorians escort you to the hydrolift and you head down through the city. To your surprise, the state rooms are in the lower levels, near the landing bays.

All over the ship, you can hear jubilant Ithorian cries. The gunfire has almost completely died away.

The elevator opens into an enormous chamber. Inside are dozens of Ithorians. They have been firing a small laser cannon down a corridor. They are cheering, as if they've just won a great victory.

"Who are you shooting at?" you yell.

"Imperial agents," one of the Ithorians says. "Bounty hunters — a man, a woman, and a Kubaz. They're retreating toward the launch bays. They won't get far!"

It must be Dengar, Udin, and Eron Stonefield. You rush down the hall, toward the launch bays. In the heavy smoke, you stumble and nearly fall. Ahead, you hear heavy gunfire and can see a door closing. It's the blast door for the launch bay. If it closes, you won't be able to get into the launch bay until the ship blasts off.

You sprint for the closing door, and try to dive through.

To dive through the door: Add your stealth# to your strength# for your confront#. Roll the 6-dice.

If your confront# is equal to or more than your roll#, add the difference +4 to your MP total. No one should be that good. You may now proceed.

If your confront# is lower than your roll#, subtract the difference from your MP total. Those closing doors can be hard on the ribs. Repeat the confront until you scramble through the doors.

You see several ships ahead. A Kubaz bounty hunter is just diving into one. Dengar, the last bounty hunter in line, is carrying a large bag — big enough to hold Grubba the Hutt! You even think you see squirming inside the bag.

Dengar whirls and fires a blaster above your head. You remember that the tractor beams are on. If this ship tries to blast off, the bounty hunters' vessel will be torn apart by the pressure of the beam.

You shout at them to stop.

Dengar leaps into the vehicle and closes the door. A laser cannon flips up on top of the ship, and swivels toward you. You drop for cover behind the nearest vehicle.

To avoid the auto-cannon: Add your skill# to your stealth# for your confront#. Roll the 6-dice.

If your confront# is equal to or more than your roll#, add the difference +6 to your MP total. Now you're dodging cannon blasts! You may proceed.

If your confront# is lower than your roll#, subtract 7MP from your MP total. Bits of plascrete hit you as shells explode overhead.

The cannon stops firing, and you roll out from behind your cover as you hear the thrusters begin to whine. You decide to take a shot at the ship's sensor dish. If the tractor beams don't stop the ship, at least it will blast off into the midst of a naval battle without any sensors.

To shoot the sensor dish: Add your weaponry# to your weapon's far-range# for your confront#. Roll the 6-dice.

If your confront# is equal to or more than your roll#, add the difference +3 to your MP total. The dish is blown off the ship. You may now proceed.

If your confront# is lower than your roll#, subtract 5MP from your MP total. You missed.

The ship blasts off. Fierce heat and white flames fill the hanger bay. You raise your shield to seek protection and duck into a corner.

To keep from getting fried: Your stealth# +1 is your confront#. Roll the 6-dice.

> *If your confront# is equal to or more than your roll#,* add 5MP to your MP total. Maybe you'd make a good fire fighter. You may now proceed.

> *If your confront# is lower than your roll#,* subtract 5MP from your MP total. So what if you singed a few hairs? They'll grow back — you hope.

The bounty hunters' vessel eases out of the bay and begins racing away. Yet in moments, you see it begin to rattle as the invisible rays of the tractor beam grasp it tightly.

You expect it to explode at any moment from the incredible forces. But the ship's pilot expertly rolls in midair, and swings back toward the *Tafanda Bay*.

You see a flash from its launch bay as a single torpedo snakes toward you. He's trying to blow the tractor beam!

You shout and run for cover as the proton torpedo hits above you. Part of the ceiling collapses. You raise your shield and dive beneath a TIE fighter.

To keep from getting flattened: Your skill# + your strength# is your confront#. Roll the 6-dice.

> *If your confront# is equal to or more than your roll#,* add the difference +4 to your MP total. You leap to safety beneath the TIE fighter. You may proceed.

> *If your confront# is lower than your roll#,* subtract 6MP from your MP total. Something heavy lands on your head, and you sit there for a moment, dazed.

You see the bounty hunters' ship arc away, up toward the sky. You leap into the TIE fighter, determined to get those bounty hunters once and for all. But as you begin to power up, a quick systems check shows that the TIE fighter has no armaments. The thing has been stripped for repairs.

Then you realize that even if you did chase the bounty hunters, and even if you shot them down, you would still lose. If Grubba dies, then Jabba will never be appeased.

You watch the bounty hunters' ship glide up into the sunlight. Then it's gone. You only hope that it doesn't get blown apart in the naval battle.

Weary and defeated, you open the blast doors and walk back up through the corridors toward the state room.

Maybe there you will find some clue that will tell you where to hunt for the young Hutt.

You wonder. The Oracle said that you could find Grubba in the state rooms. And he was right. You almost got him. You hope that in the state rooms, you will find some clue as to where the bounty hunters might have taken the Hutt.

As you walk in the halls, you suddenly find dozens of jubilant Ithorians, shouting in celebration. You remember: Despite the loss of Grubba, this mission still has been a tremendous success. "The Rebels have driven off the Imperial Navy!" they cry. Some of them recognize you and pat your back, wanting to touch their hero. You are everything to them, their sole representative from the Rebel Alliance. They act as if you have driven off the Imperial fleet single-handedly.

Right now, you are battered and bruised. Your body hurts from so many small wounds that you almost feel like you *did* drive the Empire off by yourself.

In moments, the Ithorians sweep you off your feet and carry you on their shoulders down the corridor.

"Take me to the state rooms," you shout, and in moments they stop outside a state room. They set you down. A console that was thrown up against the door as a barricade is still burning. Scorch marks and blaster holes show that the bounty hunters put up a terrible fight. All the furniture is ruined.

You inspect the room quietly for a moment, looking for any maps or records that might show where the bounty hunters went.

As you do, you hear a strained grunting, and a deep voice cries "Help! Help!" You climb over the couch and enter the room. Behind an overturned table, you find a leather bag that wriggles.

You untie the strings, and Grubba the Hutt pops out. The little brown wormlike creature gasps for air. "So, Rebel scum," he says, "are you here to save me?"

"Yeah," you answer. "I'm the one who saved you. But I was afraid that the bounty hunters had carried you off. They had a sack just like this one."

Grubba looks around quickly, in distress. "They must have gotten confused during the fight," Grubba says. "They carried off my dinner."

You remember the way that the bag squirmed in Dengar's hand. Surely, there was something alive in it.

"What was in the bag?" you ask.

"Live ghost spiders," Grubba says.

You pull a grim face. Grubba bites your knee, and says, "At least they taste better than you!"

For helping the Ithorians defeat the Empire — *and* for finding Grubba the Hutt — reward yourself 200MP (275MP for Advanced Level players).

Nice work!

THE AFTER-
MISSION

"Don't leave me here!" General Olan Dewes cried. Princess Leia was in the Ithorian jungle, amid the Bafforr groves, with Han, Luke, Chewbacca, and the droids. Momaw Nadon had brought them here, along with General Dewes, to witness Ithorian justice.

The scene was an odd one. The Oracle stood next to Dewes, staring at him with blind, white eyes. "Do not worry," the Oracle said. "We will not blind you, as you blinded me."

"Don't leave me here in this jungle!" Dewes shouted. "Kill me. It's faster."

Leia wondered. The Ithorian jungle seemed peaceful enough, aside from the hangman's trees and a few other monstrosities.

"Faster than what?" Momaw Nadon asked. "Faster than death at the hands of the Torturer?"

Olan Dewes held his head. "The trees — I hear their voices. I cannot shut them out! Please, let me go!"

Momaw Nadon smiled cruelly. "We will return for you, in a day or two. Listen to the voices of those trees. They can keep you from the shadow hunters that will otherwise eat you. Those voices can keep you alive."

"Nooooo —" Dewes cried, as the Oracle climbed into the leaf ship.

In moments, the vessel rose above the trees and hovered low over the jungle.

"You knew all along," Luke Skywalker said to the Oracle. "You *knew* that he could hear the trees."

"Yes," the Oracle said. "Many men cannot hear the voices of the Bafforr. A rare few have the gift. Such men cannot help but listen. The General Olan Dewes who came to our world years ago was a cruel, hard man. He is gone, and what is left of him will learn from the trees, learn to live in our jungles, in harmony with nature. The General Olan Dewes who learns this will be a man of peace. He will be our ally."

The sun was setting. Down among the trees, Leia could see great twisting vines, with huge trumpet-shaped yellow flowers. The flowers had opened up, inviting night insects, and the sweet fragrance of them filled the air. She gazed off toward the setting sun, just as the arrak snakes began to sing in chorus, like a thousand woodwinds rising from the jungle below.

Back aboard the *Tafanda Bay*, Han Solo lifted young Grubba in front a viewer. A holograph showed Jabba the Hutt gazing at the child in satisfaction, licking his lips with an enormous blue tongue.

"See, Jabba," Solo said, "we rescued your Ur-Damo, *again*, just like I promised." Speaking like this, on a real-time holo, was tremendously expensive. But out of gratitude, the Ithorians were footing the bill.

"Very good, Solo," Jabba said. "Bring the child to me, and I will reward you."

Han dropped Grubba and shook a finger at him. "No way! Not after the treatment we got last time. Between the sandstorms and the bounty hunters and your goons, I barely made it off Tatooine alive. This time, if you want your Ur-Damo, you can bring the reward money to *me*. Let's pick a nice, neutral planet this time. I have some old friends on Togoria."

"Agreed," Jabba said. "I will meet you on Togoria."

*   *   *

Dengar studied the tiny images of Solo and Jabba on a viewer in his ship. Jabba had patched Dengar into the call. To send a message on the communicator required great amounts of energy, and was therefore very expensive. However, Dengar didn't need much in the way of special equipment to receive a real-time call.

As Solo ended his communication, his image faded from the screen. Jabba the Hutt stared up into the viewer, as if looking at Dengar.

"Prefect Talmont assures me that you and your team can be trusted completely," the Hutt said. "You know where to find him now. Togoria. I will pay you a reward both for my Ur-Damo and for Solo. My Ur-Damo must not be harmed. But as for Solo — just bring me his head, bounty hunter. Bring me his head."

NEXT MISSION: TOGORIAN TRAP!